MICROSCOPY HANDBOOKS 10

CU00829392

Introduction to
Fluorescence Microscopy

J.S. Ploem and H.J. Tanke

Department of Cytochemistry and Cytometry
Sylvius Laboratories
University of Leiden
The Netherlands

Oxford University Press · Royal Microscopical Society · 1987

Oxford University Press, Walton Street, Oxford OX2 6DP

Oxford New York Toronto
Delhi Bombay Calcutta Madras Karachi
Petaling Jaya Singapore Hong Kong Tokyo
Nairobi Dar es Salaam Cape Town
Melbourne Auckland

and associated companies in
Beirut Berlin Ibadan Nicosia

Oxford is a trade mark of Oxford University Press

Royal Microscopical Society,
37/38 St. Clements,
Oxford OX4 1AJ

Published in the United States
by Oxford University Press, New York

British Library Cataloguing in Publication Data

Ploem, J.S.
Introduction to fluorescence microscopy. −
(Microscopy handbooks; 10)
1. Fluorescence microscopy
I. Title. II. Tanke, H.J. III. Royal
Microscopical Society IV. Series
502'.8'23 QH212.F55
ISBN 0-19-856408-2

Library of Congress in Cataloging in Publication Data
Ploem, J.S.
Introduction to fluoresence microscopy.
(Microscopy handbooks / Royal Microscopical Society: 10)
Includes index.
1. Fluorescence microscopy. I. Tanke, H.J.
II. Title. III. Series: Microscopy handbooks; 10.
QH212.F55P57 1987 578'.4 87-5539
ISBN 0-19-856408-2

Set by Grestun Graphics, Abingdon, Oxon
Printed in Great Britain by
The Alden Press, Oxford

Preface

This handbook has originated from the authors' involvement in the courses on fluorescence microscopy organized by the Royal Microscopical Society. It is based very much on the basic practice, rather than the theory, of fluorescence microscopy. The authors wish to acknowledge the contributions which have been incorporated into this handbook from students who have participated in the RMS courses and the Editor of the series for his encouragement. The technical assistance of J. Bonnet and J.C.M. Slats from the Department of Cytochemistry and Cytometry is highly appreciated. In particular, they wish to thank Professor R. Barer of the University of Sheffield, for reading the manuscript, and for making so many valuable suggestions and comments. Any errors that remain are of course the responsibility of the authors.

Leiden   J.S.P.
November 1986   H.J.T.

Contents

Introduction to fluorescence

1.1. What is fluorescence?

Hot bodies which are self-luminous solely due to their high temperature are said to be *incandescent*. All other forms of light emission are called *luminescence*. The emission of light as a result of absorbed light radiation (and not sound for example) is called *photoluminescence* and includes the processes of *fluorescence* and *phosphorescence*. Fluorescence is the property of emitting electromagnetic radiation in the form of light as the result of (and only during) the absorption of light from another source. This definition points to four important characteristics of fluorescence:

1. It is the result of the absorption of light
2. It occurs during absorption only
3. It involves the emission of light, i.e. electromagnetic radiation
4. An outside source of energy is required

These properties of fluorescence may best be explained by first considering the physical background to this type of radiation.

1.2. Physical background to fluorescence

Electrons of molecules or atoms can occur in different energy states – a ground state of minimal energy and higher energy (excitation) states. Excitation states are reached following absorption of energy, such as light radiation. In accordance with the Quantum Theory, electrons exist only in certain energy-state levels. An electron energy diagram of a fictitious molecule illustrates this principle (Fig. 1.1). The energy levels corresponding to the ground state and first excitation state are shown. Besides these permitted levels, rotational and vibrational states occur. When fluorescence occurs, energy has been absorbed resulting in excitation to a higher electronic energy state and a higher vibrational state. Subsequent return to the excitation energy state occurs with a loss of vibrational energy. Final return to the ground state may occur with a loss of energy as emitted light (fluorescence). The lifetime of the electrons in the excited state is very short: for light absorption less than 10^{-13} sec and emission about 10^{-9} sec. Compounds exhibiting fluorescence are called *fluorophores* or *fluorochromes*. Another form of luminescence where much longer lifetimes are involved, even up to seconds, is called phosphorescence. In general, molecules (or atoms) absorbing energy obey the Quantum Theory derived equation:

$$\Delta E = h\nu = \frac{hc}{\lambda} \tag{1.1}$$

(where, E = energy; h = Planck's constant; ν = frequency of light; c = velocity of light; λ = wavelength of light).

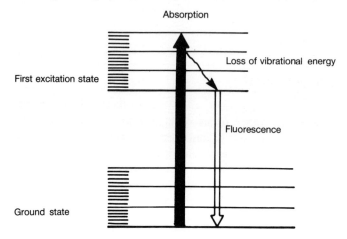

Fig. 1.1. Electronic transition diagram, illustrating the principal transitions leading to fluorescence.

Equation (1.1) states that the radiation energy is linearly proportional to the frequency of light and inversely proportional to its wavelength. In other words, the quantum of energy is greater for radiation with short wavelengths such as X-rays or ultraviolet (UV) light than for radiation with long wavelengths such as radar waves. Fluorescence studies usually involve radiation between these extremes, with wavelengths in the visible region (400–700 nm) and near UV (300–400 nm).

1.3. Spectral properties of fluorescing compounds

Fluorochromes mostly have different spectral characteristics as a result of differing electronic configurations. Absorption and emission of light take place at different regions of the light spectrum. Spectral characteristics of a typical fluorochrome are shown in Fig. 1.2. The left-hand curve – the *excitation spectrum* – is a plot of the relative total intensity of fluorescence (at a certain wavelength) obtained when the specimen is irradiated at varying wavelengths. The shape of this curve is usually identical to the shape of the absorption spectrum of pure compounds. The breadth of the spectrum can be partially explained by the fact that molecules may be excited to different vibrational energy levels, thus resulting in the absorption of differing energies (wavelengths). To obtain intense fluorescence, irradiation with light of wavelengths close to the peak of the excitation spectrum is desirable. The right-hand curve – the *emission spectrum* – shows the fluorescence intensity distribution which results from excitation at a certain wavelength.

According to Stokes' Law, the wavelength of emission is always longer than the

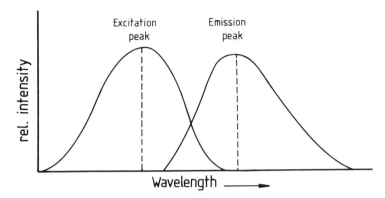

Fig. 1.2. Typical excitation and emission spectrum of a fluorophore.

wavelength of excitation. This difference in wavelength is the basis for observation of fluorescence in *fluorescence microscopy* (FM). The emission peak is always lower than the excitation peak as emitted energy is much smaller than the energy needed for excitation. Furthermore, most excitation and emission peaks overlap to a certain extent and often the emission peak is the 'mirror image' of the excitation peak.

1.4. Quantum efficiency of fluorophores

Fluorophores differ not only with regard to their spectral characteristics, but also in respect to the fluorescence intensity obtained by excitation at the optimum wavelength. The ratio between energy emitted and energy absorbed is called *quantum efficiency* (Q). Theoretically Q-values should be in the range of 0 to 1. However, in practice the measurement is often carried out relative to a standard fluorochrome (for example, rhodamine B). A number of Q-values for some common fluorochromes are given in Table 1.1. Although these values give an indication

Table 1.1. *Fluorescence quantum efficiencies in solution (20–25 °C)*

Compound	Solvent	Excitation wavelength (nm)	Q value
Acridine Orange · HC	Ethanol	366	0.46
Benzene	Ethanol	248	0.04
Chlorophyll-*a*	Ethanol	644	0.23
Chlorophyll-*b*	Ethanol	644	0.10
Eosin	Water	366	0.16
Fluorescein	Aqueous NaOH	366	0.92
Pyrene	Ethanol	313	0.72
Quinine bisulphate	Sulphuric acid	366	0.55
Rhodamine B	Ethanol	535	0.97
Thionine	Sulphuric acid	546	0.02

Many dyes have two or more absorption bands, each of which can be used for excitation.

of relative brightness of fluorescence for various fluorochromes, a number of other aspects are involved in practical microscopy: For example, the process of fading takes place – a reduction in fluorescence intensity during excitation. This can be the result of bleaching owing to photochemical reactions which cause decomposition of fluorescing molecules. The reduction in fluorescence intensity can also be the result of quenching owing to the presence of other fluorophores, oxidizing agents (oxygen) or other compounds such as halogens and salts of heavy metals which may be present in the fixative. These factors may influence the electronic configuration of the fluorescing fluorophore. For this reason preparations to be studied in FM are best stored at $4\,^{\circ}$C in the dark.

Bibliography

Lansing Taylor, D., Waggoner, A.S., Murphy, R.F., Lanni, F., and Birge, R.R. (1986). *Applications of flurorescence in the Biomedical Sciences.* Liss, New York.

Parker, C.A. (1968). *Photoluminescence of solutions: with applications to photo-chemistry and analytical chemistry.* Elsevier, Amsterdam, London, New York.

Pearse, A.G.E. (1972). *Histochemistry: theoretical and applied*, Vol. 2, (3rd edn). Churchill-Livingstone, Edinburgh.

Udenfriend, S. (1962). *Fluorescence assay in biology and medicine*, Vol. 1, Academic Press, New York.

—— (1969). *Fluorescence assay in biology and medicine*, Vol. 2, Academic Press, New York.

The fluorescence microscope

2.1. Incident or transmitted light illumination?

For the observation of fluorescence, three main components are essential: *fluoro-phore*; *light source*; *fluorescence detecting unit*. Besides these essentials, filters are required to select the appropriate excitation and emission wavelengths. A diagram of these elements is given in Fig. 2.1.

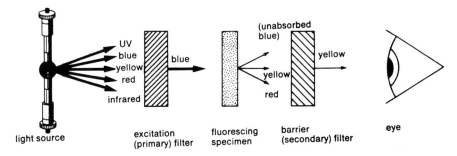

Fig. 2.1. The necessary components for the observation of fluorescence. The light source can emit more wavelengths than represented here.

An *excitation filter* (also called *primary filter*) is used to select the appropriate excitation wavelengths from the light emitted by the light source. The fluorescence specimen is illuminated and *a barrier* (*secondary*) *filter* is used to separate emitted light from unabsorbed exciting light. The fluorescence can then be observed visually, photographed or measured by a photomultiplier. In the fluorescence microscope, all these elements are present; furthermore optical lenses are needed to observe fluorescence specimens of microscopic dimensions. There are two types of illumination for FM: *transmitted* and *incident illumination*.

2.1.1. Transmitted light illumination in FM

This type of set-up (Fig. 2.2A) is the earliest applied form of FM. A condenser focuses the exciting light on to a microscope field. The emitted fluorescence is collected by the objective and observed through an eyepiece. The microscope magnification is determined by objective, eyepiece and lenses positioned between objective and eyepiece (tube lenses). Essential to this configuration is that two different lenses are used to focus the exciting light (condenser) and to collect the emitted light (objective). For optimal observation of fluorescing images, these two lenses, which have two independent optical axes, must be perfectly aligned. This is

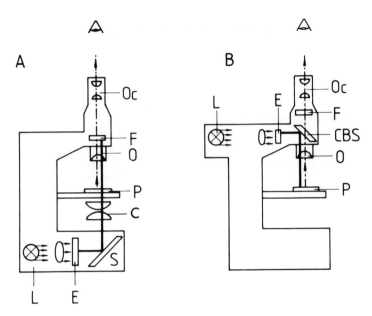

Fig. 2.2. (*A*) shows a fluorescence microscope equipped for transmitted light illumination. (*B*) shows an instrument for incident light illumination. The exciting light (—→) and the emitted fluorescence (— · — · →) are drawn for both microscopes. L = light source; E = excitation filter; S = totally reflecting mirror; CBS = chromatic beam splitter; P = preparation; O = objective; F = barrier filter; Oc = eyepiece (ocular).

not always easy to obtain and maintain in routine use. A disadvantage of transmitted light illumination by a bright field condenser is that almost all the exciting light enters the objective. Since the intensity of exciting light is often several orders of magnitude greater than that of the emitted fluorescence light, filters of very high quality are required to separate exciting from fluorescence light. Suppression of all exciting light is often not possible. Generally, a dark ground condenser is used which illuminates the specimen at such an angle that no direct exciting light enters the objective. This facilitates separation of fluorescence light and unabsorbed exciting light by means of barrier filters, provided that the numerical aperture of the objective is smaller than the numerical aperture of the dark ground condenser. Care has to be taken that blue exciting light scattered by the specimen and not completely absorbed by the barrier filter is not confused with blue fluorescence light. This problem can occur with dark ground illumination using objectives with maximum numerical aperture. A disadvantage of this type of set-up is the difficulty of changing from dark ground illumination to bright field or phase contrast illumination.

2.1.2. Incident-light illumination in FM (epi-illumination)

This type of fluorescence microscope configuration is shown in Fig. 2.2B. In this case, there is only one lens for focusing exciting light on to the specimen and collecting emitted light from the fluorescing specimen. In order to separate fluorescence emitted light from unabsorbed exciting light a special type of mirror, a *chromatic beam splitter* (CBS), sometimes known as a *dichroic mirror*, is positioned above the objective. These mirrors have a special interference coating, which reflects light shorter than a certain wavelength and transmits light of longer wavelengths. Since Stokes' Law predicts that fluorescence emitted light will have a longer wavelength than its exciting light, these mirrors effectively reflect exciting light and transmit emitted light, in this way separating the two. Any exciting light that is reflected by the specimen does not reach the eyepiece but is reflected by the CBS. In principle, the CBS acts as both excitation and barrier filter, but in practice an additional barrier filter is usually needed to eliminate any residual exciting light.

Fig. 2.3 gives an example of the separation of blue (460 nm) from green (530 nm) light. Similar chromatic beam splitters exist for separation of other regions of the light spectrum, from the UV (300 nm) to the far red (700 nm). FM with incident light has a number of advantages. Since the same lens system acts as objective and condenser, only one optical axis exists. Focusing this lens on to the specimen consequently results in proper alignment of this part of the microscope. The illuminated field is the field of view. If an oil-immersion objective is used, oil on the specimen is sufficient, whereas transmitted light illumination would also

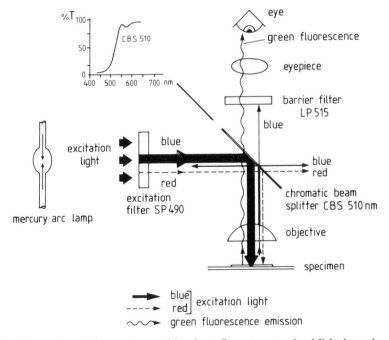

Fig. 2.3. Separation of fluorescence exciting from fluorescence emitted light by a chromatic beam splitter (CBS). Only the green fluorescing light reaches the eye. If λ lies for instance between 460 and 530 nm, the exciting light would consist of blue and UV light, and the emitted light of green and yellow light.

require oil on high aperture condensers for maximum illuminating intensity. This can easily lead to small air bubbles in the oil, which affect the intensity and evenness of the image, especially of thick specimens. Other factors that contribute to the brighter image with incident illumination are the effective use of a CBS for excitation and barrier purposes and the use of an objective as a condenser. All exciting light then is concentrated on only that part of the specimen that is within the microscope field of the objective. Epi-illumination moreover permits an easy change-over between FM and transmitted light microscopy, since the substage illumination remains readily available. For a number of applications this is very useful (such as immunofluorescence in combination with phase-contrast microscopy).

2.2. Components of the fluorescence microscope

Several important components contribute to the effective use of the fluorescence microscope, namely, the light source, filters, condenser, objective, eyepieces, etc., and their correct selection in relation to the particular application. Regrettably, selection and choice is often influenced by the restraints of a financial budget.

2.2.1. Light sources

The choice of light source is determined by the excitation spectrum of the fluorochrome and its quantum efficiency. The fluorescence intensity obtained depends on the light source emission intensity and the absorption efficiency of the fluorochrome for the emitted wavelengths. Weak fluorochromes (low Q) require more exciting light for viewing than strong fluorochromes. Some light sources (mercury lamps) have steep emission peaks in the region from 300–700 nm. Other lamps, such as the tungsten and xenon lamps, show less distinct peaks in this wavelength region. The halogen lamps show an increase of emission towards the longer wavelength side and the xenon lamps have distinct peaks in the deep red and infrared region. The emission spectra and relative intensities of a number of light sources commonly used in FM, are shown in Fig. 2.4. Lamp bulbs, especially of high-pressure type, should be mounted in strong protective housings, provided with cooling fins. The bulb should be capable of adjustment in two directions for centering. A focusing collector lens system should be available. Many housings contain an adjustable concave mirror behind the lamp; this can be used to increase the apparent size of the source. It is important to follow the manufacturer's instructions to ensure correct illumination. Lamp-housings usually have filter-holders, generally for the positioning of heat and red absorbing or reflecting filters. Heat and infrared reflecting mirrors are preferable to heat-absorbing filters since they crack less frequently. Heat and infrared filters should always be placed closer to the lamp than the coloured filters to prevent an excessive heat absorption by the latter.

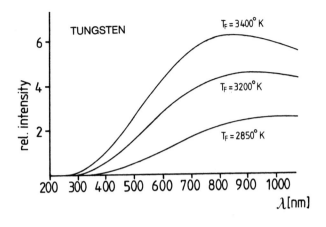

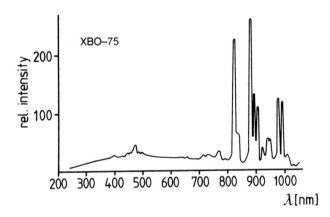

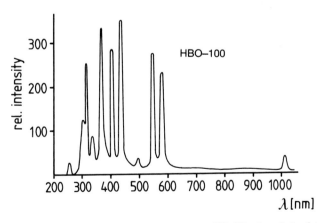

Fig. 2.4. Emission spectra of lamps commonly used for FM. Wavelength is plotted against the light intensity. T_F = Colour temperature.

Tungsten halogen lamps

The 12 V, 50 and 100 W tungsten halogen lamps are suitable and inexpensive light sources for routine investigations, provided that the specimen emits fluorescence of sufficiently high intensity. These lamps can be used for both transmitted and incident light illumination. Relatively strong fluorescein isothiocyanate (FITC) immunofluorescence can be visualized easily with these lamps. They are unsuitable for illumination with UV light however, since tungsten lamps emit very little light below 400 nm. Compared with mercury lamps they are less suitable for green excitation of red fluorescence, such as tetramethylrhodamine isothiocyanate (TRITC) immunofluorescence. The use of FITC and TRITC in immunofluorescence will be further explained in Section 1 of Chapter 4.

High-pressure mercury lamps

Mercury lamps are available as 50, 100, and 200 W lamps. The 100 W lamp has a smaller arc than the 200 W. For some types of microscopes equipped with a dark ground condenser with a central stop, the image of the HBO 100 W arc may be too small to fill the aperture and together with the central stop this may result in a too low intensity. Large research microscopes have auxiliary lenses in their light pathways for transmitted and incident illumination, so that they may be used with the various lamp types with large and small arcs and filaments. Once a fluorescence microscope has been designed for the use of a HBO 100 W lamp only, it should not be changed for use of a HBO 50 W or HBO 200 W lamp. The larger arcs of these lamps cannot be collected in the right way because they overfill the aperture of the objective. This will not result in a loss of brightness because the image intensity depends on the intrinsic brilliance of the source. However, it may result in a loss of energy so that the same result could have been obtained with a smaller, lower wattage lamp.

A mercury lamp emits a characteristic line spectrum (Fig. 2.4). Some mercury lines are 366, 405, 436, 546, and 578 nm. High-pressure mercury lamps also have a strong background continuum. In the blue region for instance, this continuum is usually much brighter than that given by a tungsten halogen lamp. If UV light or in general high-energy excitation light is required, the mercury lamps are recommended. They are relatively expensive, however, and have a limited lifetime (about 200 burning hours). Old lamps generally have only limited intensity left. A new lamp may emit considerably more light.

High-pressure xenon lamps

Unlike mercury lamps, xenon lamps emit a spectrum of rather constant intensity from UV to red. The lamp is especially effective for FITC excitation. Xenon lamps are available as 75, 150, and 450 W. The 75 W lamp has a short arc. Like mercury lamps, they are relatively expensive and have an average lifetime of 400, 1200, and

2000 burning hours for the 75, 150, and 450 W, respectively. Xenon lamps should be handled with care, because even cold lamps are, unlike mercury lamps, under pressure. Safety glasses therefore must be used during removal and replacement.

Lasers

Lasers have been used mostly in experimental studies, such as those involving flow cytometry instrumentation. They offer monochromatic radiation of very high intensity and are therefore a potential source for special-purpose fluorescence microscopy. Their relatively short lifetime and high costs limit their use in routine studies. Lasers can provide continuous output of energy or operate in a pulsed mode. With the use of short pulses of excitation energy (1 μsec to 1 nsec), fading of fluorescence can often be avoided. Furthermore, lasers are recommended for the fast automatic measurements of fluorescence signals, as is required in fluorescence scanning systems.

2.2.2. Filters

Filters are crucial for successful fluorescence microscopy. Therefore it is of the utmost importance to choose filters fitted to the application on hand. Filter choice depends on the spectral characteristics and quantum efficiency of the fluorochromes used, as well as the light source involved. To explain the properties of filters some basic aspects of light will first be discussed.

'White' light includes all spectral colours visible to the eye. These colours are classified according to their wavelength which is given in nanometres. Colours of the spectrum are seen when white light passes through a prism (Fig. 2.5). They range from violet, blue, green, to red. The range below violet is not visible to the human eye and is called *ultraviolet* (UV). The range above red is called *infrared*. A filter is used to select a certain part of the spectrum. Its effect is shown by its transmission curve. The selection of appropriate filters is illustrated for the fluorochrome FITC, for which the excitation and emission spectra are given in Fig. 2.6. It can be seen that optimum excitation is on 480 nm (blue), while the emission peak is at 525 nm (green). The excitation filter should thus be chosen to transmit blue light (400–490 nm) and to block other wavelengths. On the emission side, the barrier filter must transmit light wavelengths above 510 nm. For incident illumination this means that a CBS of about 500 nm is required. This mirror transmits light wavelengths above 500 nm (including green light) and reflects light wavelengths shorter than 500 nm (including blue light). A number of filter types (coloured glass filters, band-pass interference filters and short- and long-pass interference filters, chromatic beam splitters) are available for the selection and separation of excitation and emission wavelengths. The transmission characteristics of some of these are given in Fig. 2.7. Filters are specified by symbols/letters and numbers. Symbols/letters indicate the type of filter according to their function or characteristics. Numbers refer to the wavelength; in the case of band-pass filters

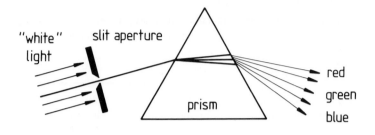

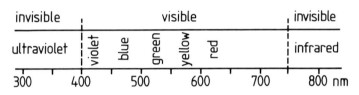

Fig. 2.5. The separation of the spectral colours of white light by use of a prism (*top*). The wavelength region of the spectrum, (*bottom*).

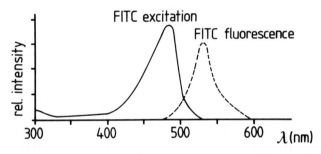

Fig. 2.6. Excitation and emission spectrum of FITC. Wavelength is plotted against the corresponding relative fluorescence intensity.

they correspond to the maximum transmission wavelength and of long-pass (LP) or short-pass (SP) filters, to the wavelength at 50 per cent of their maximum transmission. In addition, sometimes the maximum transmission value or the bandwidth (in nanometres) of a band-pass filter is given. Filters can be characterized according to their function, construction, or position in the microscope (excitation or emission side). Consequently, the terminology used by different manufacturers is quite confusing.

Production of filters

The earliest filters used were dye solutions in cuvettes and simple glass filters. Transmission characteristics of these filters were not very selective. Glass filters,

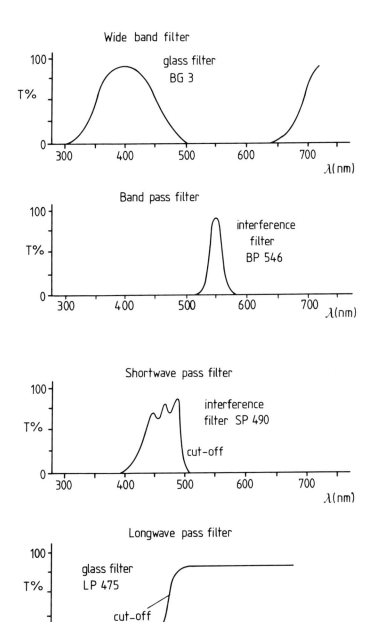

Fig. 2.7. Transmission characteristics of filters used in FM. Wavelength is plotted against the percentage transmission for each filter type.

roughly speaking, transmit light of their own colour and absorb complementary colours.

For specific excitation of one fluorescent component in a mixture of several other fluorescing components, an interference band-pass filter will be necessary. For some purposes, such as immunofluorescence, using the new fluorochromes FITC and TRITC, more selective filters are required, leading to the development of special interference filters. These are glass substrates on which thin layers of metals, metal salts, and dielectrics are deposited. When the deposition process is repeated several times, multi-layered filters are produced. Thickness and refractive index of the coatings can be chosen for selective enhancement or suppression of transmission and reflection at specific wavelengths. This is possible as a result of the interference of light rays reflected by individual layers. These multi-layered filters transmit or block certain wavelengths very specifically and effectively.

Types of filters

Abbreviations for filter types are given in Table 2.1.

Table 2.1. *Filter terminology*

Abbreviation	Filter type
BG	Blau Glas
CBS	Chromatic beam splitter
DM	Dichroic mirror
FT	Farb Teiler
GG	Gelb Glas
K	*See* LP
KP	*See* SP
LP	Long pass = K (Kanten filter)
OG	Orange Glas
RG	Rot Glas
SP	Short pass = KP (Kurz pass)
TK	Teiler Kante
UG	Ultraviolet glass
VG	Green glass

Short-wave pass filters (SP)

TERMINOLOGY: SP, KP

These are almost exclusively interference filters. They transmit lower wavelengths and effectively block higher wavelengths. These properties make them suitable as excitation filters when combined with LP filters. In such combinations, they are preferable to glass filters (for example, BG-type filters), since they generally do not leak unwanted excitation light. An LP–SP combination also serves as an effective emission selection filter. This is especially useful for sequential observation of two-colour fluorescence with minimal overlap. Short-pass filters, like all interference filters, are expensive. In comparison with the older types of interference band-pass filters, SP filters have a very high transmission. Transmission curves of common SP filters are given in Fig. 2.8.

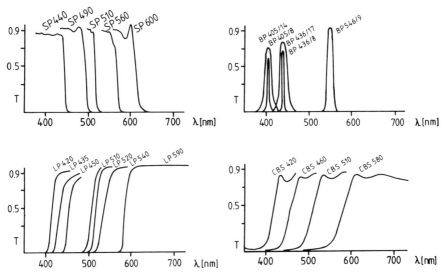

Fig. 2.8. Transmission characteristics of short-wave pass filters (SP), long-wave pass filters (LP), band-pass filters (BP), and chromatic beam splitters (CBS).

Long-wave pass filters (LP)

TERMINOLOGY: LP, K, GG, OG, RG

These types of filter have a high transmission for the longer wavelengths (90 per cent or higher) and effectively block shorter wavelengths. The LP filters are predominantly used as barrier filters; in combination with short-pass interference filters they are also applied as excitation filters. Until recently, LP filters were glass-type filters. Interference-type filters are now being manufactured. Some glass LP filters may show autofluorescence at very high intensities. Used as barrier filters in routine FM, this will generally not cause problems. Transmission curves of long-pass filters are given in Fig. 2.8.

Band-pass filters (BP)

TERMINOLOGY: It is difficult to give a general terminology because manufacturers use their own code numbers

Band-pass filters usually transmit one particular region (band) of the light spectrum. The glass filters with band-pass characteristics, still in use, are the BG and UG filters. They have rather broad transmission characteristics. Band-interference filters are more selective. A disadvantage of these filters in the past was their low transmission value (30–60 per cent). This problem has been overcome. At present band-pass filters with high transmissions (90 per cent) and very narrow-band characteristics can be produced for selective excitation of fluorochromes (line filters). Consequently, BP filters are mainly used as excitation filters, especially when mercury arc lamps are used as excitation light source. Depending on the quality, they vary in price. Transmission curves for some common BP filters are given in Fig. 2.8.

Chromatic beam splitters (CBS)

TERMINOLOGY: CBS, FT, TK, Dichroic mirror

The characteristics of a CBS are normally given for incident light at 45°. Standard CBS are available at 400 or 410 nm for UV excitation, at 455 nm or 460 nm for violet excitation, at 500 nm or 510 nm for blue excitation, and at 580 nm for green excitation. With these four standard excitation modules, the commonly used excitation combinations for incident light fluorescence microscopy are obtained (see Table 2.2). A CBS reflects light of wavelengths shorter than the specified wavelength and transmits light of longer wavelengths. It should be emphasized, that depending on the application, these filters can be modified for improved results. Chromatic beam splitters should not be confused with normal 50–50 per cent beam splitters. These mirrors, apart from the light loss, transmit and reflect equal amounts of light, irrespective of the wavelength. The transmission curves of some standard CBS types are given in Fig. 2.8.

Table 2.2. *Characteristics of chromatic beam splitters* (CBS).[a]

Excitation	Excitation filter	CBS	Barrier filter
UV	3 mm UG 1	CBS 400 or CBS 410	LP 430
Violet	3 mm BG 3 + SP 425 or BP 405	CBS 455 or CBS 460	LP 470
Blue	2 × SP 490 + 2 mm LP 455	CBS 500 or CBS 510	LP 515
Green	BP 546 or SP 560 + LP 515	CBS 580	LP 590

[a] Abbreviations of filters are given in Table 2.1.

Other filter types

Besides the filter types already mentioned, others are used in fluorescence micro-scopy. Amongst them are *neutral-density filters* and *heat-protection filters*. Heat-protection filters can absorb or reflect heat. An example of a heat-absorbing filter is given in Fig. 2.9. Heat-protection filters are positioned in front of the light source to reduce heat transfer to the actual exciting filters. The Calflex filter reflects in-frared radiation. Neutral-density filters have no specific absorption characteristics; they generally transmit all wavelengths but reduce the light intensity by absorption and/or reflection. Their transmission values vary to almost 100 per cent. The very dark (low transmittance) filters are almost always reflection filters, since glass filters would absorb too much light and become overheated. These filters are used for reduction of exciting light energy to avoid fading of fluorochromes during examination.

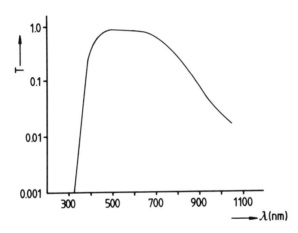

Fig. 2.9. Transmission characteristics of a heat-protection filter.

2.2.3. Use and maintenance of filters

Filters must be treated with care. Interference filters especially are damaged easily. Although most filters have a protective layer of glass or plastic, it is advisable to handle filters only with lens tissue. If two or more filters must be inserted in an illuminator, a thin metal ring should be used to separate them and avoid scratching. Dirty filters can be cleaned (gently) with xylene or with lens cleaner, provided that a glass coating is present. The lifetime is prolonged if needless irradiation of the filters is avoided in actual use. A shutter positioned in the lamp-housing can be closed for this purpose. Filters are best stored at room temperature in a dry, closed compartment with silica gel.

2.2.4. Condensers, objectives, and eyepieces

Transmitted light FM with bright field condensers was forsaken almost completely with the introduction of the *dark ground condenser*. With this condenser, illuminating light is directed towards the specimen at such an oblique angle, that no direct exciting light enters the objective. With this type of illumination, the only light reaching the objective is scattered light. For FM, this facilitates the separation of exciting and emitted light. In Fig. 2.10 (left) the light-beam path is shown for this type of condenser. A disadvantage of the system is the loss of light owing to the central stop. This has led to the development of the *Tiyoda condenser* (Fig. 2.10, right). This condenser directs almost all of the exciting light towards the specimen. The numerical aperture (NA) of the dark ground condenser should be higher than the NA of the objective. In transmitted light illumination, an oil-immersion condenser is often used as it has a high numerical aperture. This assures

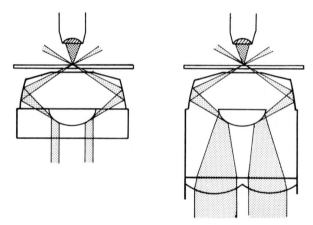

Fig. 2.10. The light pathways are shown for a normal dark ground condenser (*left*) and a Tiyoda dark ground condenser (*right*).

a high light yield, since the fluorescence intensity is proportional to the square of the illuminating numerical aperture. Examples are the oil-immersion condensers with a NA of 1.20 to 1.40. The use of a dry condenser is more convenient if the fluorescence is sufficiently strong (NA of 0.80 to 0.95 are available).

For incident light illumination, the *objective* serves as both condenser and objective. The NA therefore becomes of major importance. The fluorescence intensity now becomes proportional to the fourth power of the NA of the objective. The maximum NA which can be obtained in an objective depends on the refractive index of the medium between the front lens of the objective and cover-slip (air, water, glycerine, or immersion oil), as is illustrated in Fig. 2.11. Depending on the applications, a variety of objectives are used in fluorescence microscopy. Examples are:

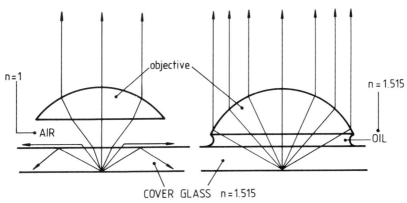

Fig. 2.11. Influence of the refractive index of the immersion medium (air and oil) on the theoretical maximum of the numerical aperture.

A. Low-to-moderate power (10–40 X) dry objectives (NA up to 0.80). Convenient to work with, long free working distance, large depth of focus.

B. Moderate-to-high power (40–100 X) oil-immersion objectives (NA up to 1.30). Lenses of high resolution and extremely high light-gathering power, but limited depth of focus and free working distance. Special low fluorescence immersion media should be used.

C. Glycerine and water-immersion lenses (NA up to 1.20). Minimal autofluorescence of immersion medium. Convenient to use (especially water-immersion lenses). Relatively high brightness achievable.

Objectives are always chosen in combination with *eyepieces*. The eyepiece further magnifies the image to the desired dimensions and should be selected to match the correction state of the objective (Fig. 2.12). Numerous eyepiece types are available varying in complexity (Fig. 2.12A, B). Compensating eyepieces are generally recommended for use with apochromatic, semi-apochromatic and high-power achromatic objectives in order to correct for residual colour errors (chromatic difference of magnification). Eyepieces designed for long eye clearance are available for spectacle-wearers and special format-indicating graticules may be provided for photomicrography. Binocular microscopes require specially-matched pairs of eyepieces. In choosing objective–eyepiece combinations, it is important to realize that the brightness of fluorescence (i.e. the fluorescence per unit area) is inversely proportional to the magnification squared. Maximum brightness is thus obtained at minimum eyepiece magnification and maximum numerical aperture of the objective.

Bibliography

Bradbury, S. (1984). *An introduction to the optical microscope*, Microscopy Handbooks 1, Royal Microscopical Society.

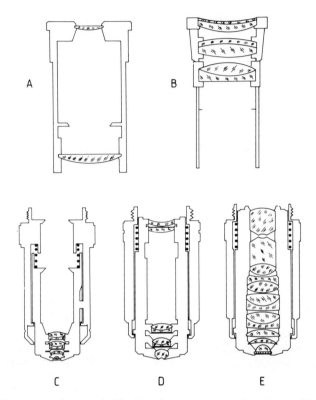

Fig. 2.12. Common eyepieces and objectives for microscopes. A = Huygens' low-power eye-piece; B = wide-angle eyepiece; C = achromatic objective; D = plan objective; E = planapo objective.

Holz, H.M. (1975). *Worthwhile facts about fluorescence microscopy*, Carl Zeiss, Oberkochen, West Germany. K41-005-e.

James, J. (1976). *Light microscopic techniques in biology and medicine*, Martinus Nijhoff Medical Division, Amsterdam.

Koch, K.F. (1974). *Fluorescence microscopy: instruments, methods and applications* Leitz, Wetzlar, West Germany.

Olympus Optical Co. Ltd (1982). *The use of the Olympus Fluorescence Microscope*, Tokyo, Japan.

Pearse, A.G.E. (1972). *Histochemistry: theoretical and applied*, Vol 2, (3rd edn). Churchill-Livingstone, Edinburgh.

Practical fluorescence microscopy

3.1. Installing the fluorescence microscope

The main components of two commercially available fluorescence microscopes are shown in Fig. 3.1. These are:

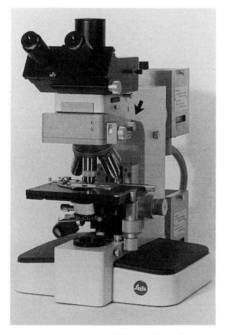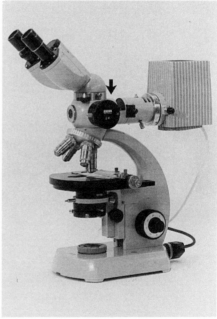

Fig. 3.1. Two commercially available fluorescence microscopes.

Microscope stand with stage and low-voltage transmitted illumination.
Vertical illuminator with sliding and revolving filter holders (arrows in Fig. 3.1).
Lamp-housing.
Revolving nose-piece with objectives.
Eyepieces.
Condenser.

These components are attached by bayonet fittings and can be easily detached. The alignment and adjustment of modern fluorescence microscopes is not very difficult and should therefore be performed before each use. First of all, it is necessary to check the adjustment and centration of the light source. A correctly aligned lamp gives even *illumination* of the entire microscope field (*Koehler* illumination).

Actually in Koehler illumination it is not the light source itself, but an optically generated homogeneous light field that functions as a light source. This field is obtained by using an auxiliary lens (collector) positioned just in front of the light source. In Fig. 3.2 the principle of Koehler illumination is illustrated for incident illumination. The luminous field diaphragm sets the illumination field size, thus avoiding exposure of regions of the specimen which are not observed. This results in a reduction of glare, a considerably higher contrast and, in the case of fluorescence, a reduced exposure to exciting light.

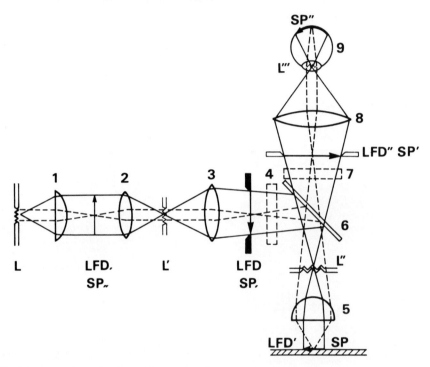

Fig. 3.2. Image formation in a microscope adjusted for Koehler illumination. ————: imaging rays; - - - - - -: illuminating rays. L = light source; LFD = luminous field diaphragm; SP = specimen. L', L", L''', LFD', LFD", SP' and SP" are forward images; LFD,, and SP, and SP,, are backward images. 1 = collector; 2 and 3 = auxiliary lenses; 4 = excitation filter; 5 = objective (the condenser in epi-illumination); 6 = chromatic beam splitter; 7 = barrier filter; 8 = eyepiece; 9 = eye.

It has to be noted that in FM, the specimen behaves as a new light source so that the objective aperture will be filled, no matter what the illuminating aperture may be. The resolving power is thus the maximum obtainable for the objective used. The first forward image of the specimen is called the *primary image* (SP'). The final image of the specimen (SP") is on the retina of the eye and thus seen. The principle of Koehler illumination is the same for epi- and transmitted illumination.

To achieve Koehler illumination in *epi-illumination*, the lamp must be adjustable in two axes. Movement of the collector lens is performed to focus the arc in the back focal plane of the objective. Centering is generally done by movement of the lamp. For these adjustments it is helpful to first set the microscope for Koehler illumination in transmitted light and place a piece of paper onto the microscope stage. The projection of the light-spot from the substage condenser onto the paper is the reference point for the optical axis. Subsequently, one of the objectives is removed. The projection of the arc on the piece of paper is then focused and centered. Most lamp-housings have mirrors in the back that can be centered and focused. Some microscopes are provided with a small ground glass screen on which the arc can be projected to facilitate Koehler illumination. Generally, illumination should be equal in all parts of the field (i.e. Koehler illumination). Sometimes, however, it may be useful to have a very high local excitation intensity by imaging the arc of the lamp on the specimen observed. This is called *critical illumination*. The exciting light passes through a field diaphragm which can be centered and adjusted to the size of the object being studied. Minimizing the field diaphragm avoids fading along the edge of the field (important in microfluorometry). The transmitted light should be adjusted to Koehler illumination or appropriate phase-contrast illumination by focusing the condenser and adjusting the phase annulus if necessary. Finally, the microscopist should adjust the eyepiece separation for optimal binocular viewing. Most binocular microscopes have one fixed and one focusable eyepiece. While looking through the fixed eyepiece, focus the image as sharply as possible, using the fine adjustment. Then, without touching the fine adjustment, look through the other eyepiece and focus it sharply by the eyepiece-focusing device.

Some noteworthy points include the following:

- FM is best performed in a darkened room, especially in situations where weakly fluorescing images have to be observed.
- FM will be performed with minimum fatigue if the eyes are relaxed and at, or near, infinity focus.
- Exciting light should be blocked by shutters when the microscope is not used for long periods. This prevents unnecessary heating and damage to interference filters.
- Microscopes require regular cleaning and maintenance. Lenses and other optical parts should be cleaned only with lens tissue to prevent scratching. If necessary some xylene may be used, though only sparingly and for a very short time.
- When not in use, microscopes should be protected against dust.

3.2. Choice of the correct filter combinations

Factors important in choosing excitation and emission filters include the following.

1. Fluorochrome. Excitation and emission filters should ideally match excitation and emission spectra of the fluorochrome. These spectra also determine the chromatic beam splitter needed, when incident illumination is used. Especially for fluorochromes of low quantum efficiency and for performing fluorescence photomicrography, filters must have high transmissions for maximum fluorescence intensity.

2. Fluorochrome environment. In the ideal situation, a fluorescing object is present in a non-fluorescing background. In this case wide band filters can be used since there is only one object that fluoresces. This is uncommon, however. Often other fluorescing compounds are present in the specimen. This can be due to auto-fluorescence of the background or fluorescence of a second dye of a different colour. The latter can show disturbing colour overlap. Under these conditions specific narrow-band excitation and selective emission filters are required. This is discussed in more detail in Chapter 4.

3. Excitation light source. The emission spectrum of the light source will favour the use of certain filters and exclude the use of others: recently, very narrow band-pass filters with high transmissions have been developed to select one particularly strong mercury line, for instance BP 365 and the BP 546. Obviously they can be applied with xenon lamps as well. However, since the peak transmission wavelength value is much less critical for these lamps (because of their rather flat emission characteristics), sometimes a wider band-pass filter of slightly different wavelength provides a cheaper alternative.

4.Financial budget. Unfortunately this is often one of the most important factors. Interference filters are expensive and have limited lifetimes. If the fluorochromes to be observed are bright and there is minor interference from background fluorescence, excellent results can be obtained with inexpensive glass filters (such as BG 12 for strong FITC fluorescence). The choice of filters is usually determined by a combination of the factors listed above.

3.3. Choice of condensers, objectives, and eyepieces

3.3.1. Condenser

For transmitted light, either bright field or dark ground condensers are available. In most cases a dark ground condenser is used because it facilitates separation of fluorescence-emitted light from unwanted exciting light, which is suppressed by a barrier filter. The exciting filter and the high wavelength barrier filter should be selected to give the best results in relation to the optics used and the properties of the specimen. Dark ground condensers make barrier filtering easier than bright field condensers. In transmitted light illumination, maximum fluorescence intensity can only be achieved with a condenser of high numerical aperture. This consequently requires oil-immersion condensers. Dry condensers are preferred, especially for routine work.

3.3.2. Objective and eyepiece

Especially in incident FM, the obtained result strongly depends on the choice of objective and eyepiece. Not all objectives are suitable for FM as they are sometimes equipped with many extra lenses for correction of imaging errors. These extra lenses reduce transmission and thus the brightness of the fluorescence. Generally, microscope objectives are classified according to their state of *correction*. Correction can be carried out for chromatic aberration; this means that the focal length for different colours of light is different. Other corrections are for the curvature of field (a phenomenon which occurs especially at high magnifications, in which the centre and periphery of the microscopic field cannot be focused simultaneously) and the spherical aberrations. The most commonly used lenses and their specifications are given in the following list:

Achromat (no specification generally indicates an achromat). These are objectives with a rather simple correction for chromatic aberration. The focal length of the colours red and blue are equalized.

Fluorite (semi-apochromat, fluotar, FL neofluar). Some lenses in fluorite systems are made of fluorspar, which results in better correction for chromatic aberration. These lenses generally have a better transmission for UV light.

Apochromat (APO). These have the best correction for chromatic and spherical aberration. A complete correction has been obtained for the colours violet, blue, and red. This type of objective gives the best sharpness, contrast, and resolution.

Plan (PL, NPL, EF, flat field objectives). When sharpness is required for the entire field of view (photomicrography), a plan objective is often used. In these objectives the curvature of field has been eliminated.

Plan apochromat (Plan APO). The corrections of an apochromat and the plan objective are combined in one objective.

Quartz objective (Ultrafluar). The lenses of these objectives are made of quartz for UV microscopy.

For FM, achromats or fluorites are very suitable. It is not necessary to use an apochromat as usually only one or two colours are observed simultaneously in fluorescence microscopy. Plan apochromats generally contain many correction lenses, which result in a loss of light intensity. Other information which can usually be found engraved on objectives includes the following:

· The optical tube length; in most cases 160 mm (or 170 mm), sometimes infinity.

· The need or otherwise for a cover glass, and where required the cover glass thickness.

· The immersion medium (oil, glycerine, water); no specification indicates a dry objective.

· The numerical aperture (NA).

· The specification for phase-contrast microscopy or microscopy with polarized light, etc.

The observed intensity of fluorescence is proportional to the square of the NA of both condenser and objective for transmitted illumination, and to the fourth power of the NA of the objective for incident illumination. Furthermore, the observed brightness (fluorescence per unit area) is inversely proportional to the square of the total magnification. What this implies in epi-illumination is illustrated in the following calculations: Compare a 25X, NA = 0.75 oil-immersion objective with a 10X eyepiece, and a 40X, NA = 1.30 oil-immersion objective with a 6.3X eyepiece. They have the same total magnification of 350X. The brightness of the second combination is a factor of nine higher! The general policy for selecting an objective-eyepiece combination is first to determine the total magnification and subsequently select the objective with the highest NA. The total magnification is then obtained by choosing the appropriate eyepiece.

Bibliography

Bradbury, S. (1984). *An introduction to the optical microscope*, Microscopy Handbooks, 1. Royal Microscopical Society.

Determan, H. and Lepusch, F. (1969). *The microscope and its application*. Leitz, Wetzlar, West Germany. 512–69b/engl.

Jenaer Glaswerk Schott, *Filter catalogue: Farb und Filter Glas*. Mainz, West Germany.

Moellring, F.K. *Microscopy from the very beginning*. Carl Zeiss, Oberkochen, West Germany.

Immunofluorescence

4.1. Principles of immunofluorescence

The immunofluorescence technique is one of the most commonly used biomedical applications of fluorescence microscopy (FM). The wide application of immuno-fluorescence (IF) and the resulting demand for improved equipment stimulated the development of high-quality lenses and filters by the optics industry and had a great impact on fluorescence microscopy in general. Special attention will be given here to the problems encountered in IF and their possible solutions.

In IF, use is made of a specific reaction between an antibody and an antigen. Antibodies are immunoglobulins, produced by animals and humans as a natural defence mechanism against invasion of foreign compounds (antigens) such as bacteria, viruses, proteins, etc. When a body is invaded by bacteria, the body will recognize the bacteria as foreign, whereupon the production of antibodies is initiated. Combination of the antibody with the antigen will lead to the neutraliz-ation of the antigen. The antigen–antibody combination is specific; that is, a certain antibody will only react with the antigen which stimulated its production. Thus, if antibodies have been produced against, for instance, the measles virus, these anti-bodies will not react with polio virus.

Antibodies can be produced in the laboratory by repeated inoculations of suspensions or solutions of antigen into an animal. The rabbit is frequently used for this purpose. The intravenous method is most commonly used for the inocu-lation of relatively large doses of antigen over a period of several weeks. After termination of the inoculation schedule, the serum will contain a large quantity of antibodies. Whole serum can be used for antigen–antibody reaction, but most investigators prefer more purified immunoglobulin fractions. Presently, antibodies can be made very specific to react with only one particular protein. By fusion of myeloma cells with spleen cells from immunized animals, clones that synthesize one type of antibody (monoclonal antibody) can be prepared.

Antibodies can be covalently labelled with fluorochromes without undergoing a significant loss of immunological specificity. Antibodies labelled with fluoro-chromes are called *conjugates*. In an immunofluorescence test such a conjugate is incubated with cells or tissue. A few drops of conjugated serum containing anti-bodies are layered over a smear or section containing antigen. The antibodies will react in a specific way with the antigens; the antibody will be precipitated and be fixed in place. After removing excess antibodies by washing, the preparations can be examined by FM and the sites of the reaction established. The principal reac-tions for this test are shown in Fig. 4.1. The normal antigen–antibody reaction and the labelling of the antibody are shown in Fig. 4.1A and Fig. 4.1B, respectively.

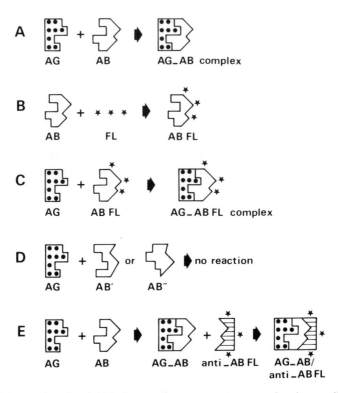

Fig. 4.1. Main reactions involved in immunofluorescence. A = normal antigen–antibody reaction; B = labelling with fluorochrome (FL); C = reaction of labelled antibody with antigen results in fluorescence* after excitation; D = no reaction; E = indirect reaction.

The antigen–antibody reaction is very specific; the antigen will not react with antibodies that do not fit its structure (FIG. 4.1D).

In Fig. 4.1C the antigen reacts with the labelled antibody; its reaction product can be seen in the fluorescence microscope. This reaction requires only one incubation step and is called the *direct method*. If the direct method results in a very weak fluorescence, a second incubation step can be applied. This is explained in Fig. 4.1E. This *indirect method* consists first of an incubation of the antigen with antibody, after which follows an incubation with conjugate against the antibody. As one antigen usually binds with several antibodies, the number of sites for subsequent binding with a conjugate is larger than in the direct test. Consequently, the fluorescence will be stronger in the indirect method. The conjugate that is used in the second incubation usually consists of a serum against the animal species in which the first antibody was raised. Therefore, only a few types of sera need to be labelled for the indirect test, which is an advantage over the direct method, which requires labelling of all antibodies used.

Antigens can also be fluorescently labelled to demonstrate antibodies, receptors, etc. The power of the technique is that the specificity of immunology is combined with the sensitivity of fluorescence.

Fluorochromes which can be used for labelling are the fluorescein and rhodamine derivatives. The most frequently used are fluorescein isothiocyanate (FITC) and tetramethylrhodamine isothiocyanate (TRITC). The absorption light is used for spectra of FITC are shown in Fig. 2.6 on p. 12. Green exciting light is used for TRITC excitation, which then emits a red fluorescence.

Problems in IF microscopy mainly arise from *non-specific fluorescence*. This sometimes originates from non-specific reactions of the conjugate, which may be avoided by improving incubation conditions or by the use of other more specific conjugates. Non-specific fluorescence may also be due to *primary* or *secondary fluorescence* of cells or tissues. Primary fluorescence is defined as the native fluorescence (*autofluorescence*) owing to excitation of certain cell or tissue constituents. Compounds such as tryptophan, flavine, lipofuchsin, or porphyrin show autofluorescence. Most of them fluoresce blue or green when excited with UV light, although red fluorescence is sometimes seen (porphyrins). Also, fixatives such as glutaraldehyde may induce fluorescence by forming aromatic fluorescing compounds when reacting with cells (a form of secondary fluorescence). These compounds may fluoresce in any part of the visible spectrum.

Non-specific primary and secondary fluorescence can be suppressed by selective excitation of the fluorochrome used in the IF technique. A specific excitation filter will enhance the fluorescence of the IF fluorochrome to a greater extent than the non-specific fluorescence, thus improving the contrast. This is achieved by using excitation filters with very narrow transmission characteristics matching the excitation peak of the fluorochrome of the conjugate. This will lead predominantly to an improved contrast but unfortunately also to a reduced absolute fluorescence intensity since only a small part of the spectrum is used for excitation. Thus, one often has to compromise between contrast and intensity.

Appropriate selection of emission (barrier) filters can further improve contrast. Emission filters should primarily select the emission wavelengths of the fluorochrome and suppress non-specific fluorescence. An example of selective narrow excitation is shown in Fig. 4.2 for FITC conjugates. Although excitation and emission curves partly overlap, there need be no overlap if the proper filters are used.

Whereas early IF was performed using UV excitation and later with a BG 12 glass filter, selective excitation of FITC can now be realized by using a LP 450 and SP 490 filter combination or even a LP 475 and SP 490 combination. This can lead to a greatly improved contrast, especially for FITC-IF in tissue sections. Another example of selective excitation is the specific green excitation of TRITC with a narrow band-pass filter, the BP 546 for red IF. This filter effectively selects the strong 546 nm mercury line with 80–90 per cent transmission. The selective excitation and specific selection of emission wavelengths is also used in the so-called *two-wavelength excitation method*. This technique is used if two fluorochromes (such as FITC and TRITC) have to be observed sequentially with minimal disturbing

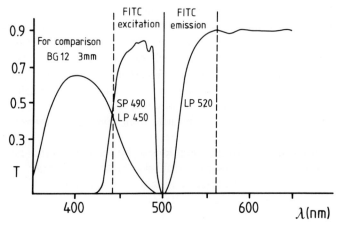

Fig. 4.2. FITC excitation using wide-band excitation (BG 12) or narrow-band excitation (LP 450 + SP 490). The LP 520 emission-filter characteristic is also shown.

interference between the two fluorochromes. Fig 4.3 shows the filter combinations which are used for the sequential excitation of FITC and TRITC.

Narrow-band blue light is used for FITC excitation. Although this is not the optimum excitation wavelength of TRITC, this will lead to some red fluorescence

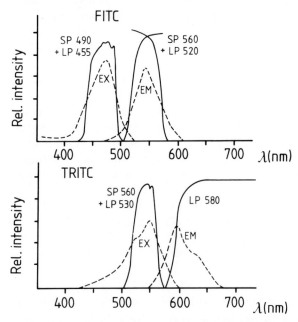

Fig. 4.3. Two-wavelength excitation of double-stained IF specimens (FITC and TRITC). Transmission characteristics of filters are shown (————) simultaneously with the spectral characteristics of the fluorochrome. (- - - - - - -).

from TRITC. A green selection filter (BP type or LP + SP type) can effectively select only the green emission light. TRITC is excited with narrow-band green light, with negligible excitation of FITC. A LP 580 filter is suitable for the red emission of TRITC. Since the two-wavelength excitation method has many applications, special epi-illuminators have been developed to observe two-colour fluorescence sequentially in a rapid and convenient way. With one movement the whole filter-set,

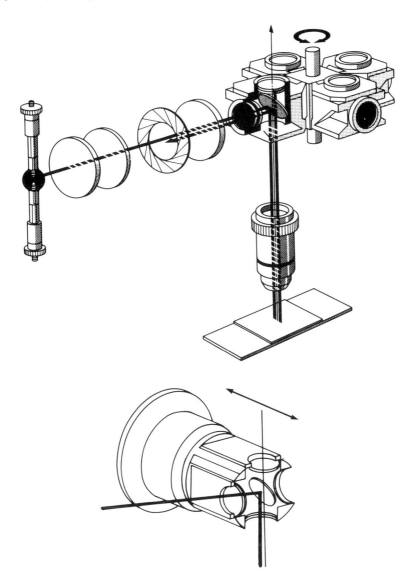

Fig. 4.4. Two examples of epi-illuminators. Filter changing by rotating filter-holder (*top*); a system in which filter-sets are changed by sliding the filter-holder (*bottom*).

including excitation, CBS, and barrier filters can be changed. Fig. 4.4 shows two examples of modern multiple excitation with epi-illuminators.

Besides special filter combinations, the success of IF depends very much on the choice of objectives. As mentioned in Chapter 2, the total magnification of objective and eyepiece should be as low as possible and the NA as high as possible. This has led to the development of lenses of moderate magnification and maximum NA (40X with NA = 1.30; 63X with NA = 1.30). To achieve this high NA, oil-immersion lenses must be used, which is not always convenient. Water-immersion objectives of reasonably high NA are also available (25X with NA = 0.60; 50X with NA = 1.0; 100X with NA = 1.20) for clean and rapid inspection of IF preparations.

4.2. Preparation problems encountered in IF

For high-quality microscopy of immunofluorescently-stained specimens, some steps in the preparation of reagents and the treatment of the specimen are important.

4.2.1. Preparation of conjugates

Generally, antibodies raised in immunized animals or monoclonal antibodies from cultures are covalently labelled with fluorochromes such as FITC and TRITC. The degree of labelling is expressed as the *F/P ratio*; this is the ratio of the number of fluorochrome molecules to the number of protein molecules. In the past, *F/P* ratios of many conjugates were high (5-10), since the more fluorochrome molecules, the brighter the fluorescence image. However, strongly-labelled antibodies tend to lose their immunological specificity and therefore may show non-specific reactions. With improvement of optics for FM the sensitivity of the IF method has increased considerably. The *F/P* ratios of conjugates are at present much lower. Conjugates with an *F/P* of 1-2 are generally recommended for most applications. It is important that after labelling of the antibodies excess of unbound fluorochrome is removed by gel-filtration techniques, since free fluorochrome will increase non-specific staining. Once prepared, conjugates should be stored in a suitable concentration (1-10 mg protein/ml phosphate-buffered saline) at $-20°$ or freeze dried. Since repeated freeze-drying and thawing leads to breakage of the covalent bond between fluorochrome and protein, it is recommended that a prepared batch of conjugate is dispensed into micro-cups, which can be thawed one by one for use. The concentration of protein that should be used for the labelling strongly depends on the applications. Generally, the lowest possible concentration of conjugate should be used to avoid non-specific reactions.

4.2.2. Preparation of the specimen

If a fixation procedure for the specimen is included, fixatives which do not induce fluorescence in the specimen are preferred. Most commonly-used fixatives are ethanol, methanol, acetone, formaldehyde, glutaraldehyde (in low concentrations), and carbodiimides. For intracellular immunofluorescence (plasma cells) fixation in 5 per cent acetic acid in ethanol at $-20°C$ is very suitable. After every step in the staining reaction, the preparations must be washed with several changes of buffered saline solution and should generally not be allowed to dry before being embedded in medium. This is important to keep the level of non-specific fluorescence low. The preparations are mostly embedded in a wet mount of glycerol and phosphate-buffered saline (PBS; pH 7.2) in a ratio of 9:1 (v/v). The cover-glass is mounted with a xylene-based embedding medium. The glycerol in the embedding medium enhances the fluorescence of most fluorochromes. The use of paraffin or nail polish is not recommended. The former cracks at $-20°C$; the latter sometimes contains fluorescent compounds which may leak into the embedding medium. Anti-bleaching agents such as DABCO (1,4-diazobicyclo-2,2,2-octane), N-propyl gallate and p-phenylenediamine can be added to the mounting medium.

Bibliography

Goldman, M. (1968). *Fluorescent antibody methods*. Academic Press, New York.
Holborrow, E.J. (1970). *Immunofluorescence*. Blackwell Scientific Publishers, Oxford.
Nairn, R.C. (1976). *Fluorescent protein tracing*. (4th edn). Churchill-Livingstone, Edinburgh.
Ploem, J.S. (1973). Immunofluorescence microscopy. In *Immunopathology of the skin: labeled antibody studies*, (ed. E.H. Beutner, T.P. Chorzelski, S.F. Bean, and R.E. Jordan), p. 248. Dowden, Hutchinson and Ross, Stroudsburg, Pennsylvania.
Wick, G., Baudner, S. and Herzog, F. (1978). *Immunofluorescence*. Medizinische Verlaggesellschaft, Marburg, West Germany.

5

Quantitative fluorescence microscopy

Use of fluorescence measurements to obtain quantitative information on the presence of fluorescing substrates is steadily increasing, not only in the field of bio-medical research, but also in the field of coal petrology and electronic industries. For these measurements instrumentation is available which can be categorized into three types. The first and most conventional type of *microfluorometer*, consists of a fluorescence microscope with a special optical configuration. A light-sensing device (photomultiplier) is added for measuring the light. Total fluorescence of objects is measured. The second category (the *scanning microfluorometer*) is in-tended for special applications and is usually equipped with computer-controlled stepping motors to move the microscope stage in horizontal and vertical directions. This permits measurement of local fluorescence intensities. Essentially this method of measurement is also possible with microfluorometers equipped with a scanning light sensor, for example a television camera. Finally, the measurement of a large number of fluorescing objects within a relatively short time can be achieved using *flow cytometers*. Before giving a brief description of the instrumentation and measuring principles of these systems, some remarks are necessary which apply to fluorescence measurements in general.

5.1. Theoretical background to fluorescence measurements

If light of intensity I_0 is directed through a solution some absorption of the inci-dent radiation will occur. The light not absorbed is transmitted by the substance and can be denoted I. Thus $(I_0 - I)$ represents the light energy absorbed by the specimen. As a result of the absorption, fluorescence may occur. The intensity of the fluorescence is related to the absorption,

$$F = Q (I_0 - I) \tag{5.1}$$

(where, F = fluorescence intensity; I_0 = light intensity before absorption; I = light intensity after absorption; Q = quantum efficiency).
According to Lambert's law, the absorption (A) is:

$$A = - \log(I/I_0) \longrightarrow I = I_0 \, e^{-A} \tag{5.2}$$

Then the fluorescence intensity can be written as:

$$F = Q (I_0 - I_0 \, e^{-A}) \longrightarrow F = Q I_0 (1 - e^{-A}) \tag{5.3}$$

When A approaches zero, e^{-A} approaches 1 and F approaches zero.

When A approaches ∞, e^{-A} approaches 0. Then $F = QI_0$.

When A is very small $1 - e^{-A}$ approaches A. Then $F = AQI_0$.

A can also be written as kc, where k is a constant and c the concentration. For low concentrations, $F = kcQI_0$, thus the fluorescence intensity is directly proportional to the concentration. For high concentrations, $F = QI_0$, which is independent of concentration.

Important conclusions from these equations are that the fluorescence intensity is directly related to the intensity of the excitation light and for quantitative measurements of fluorescence, I_0 must be kept constant. Further, the intensity of fluorescence is directly proportional to absorbance but only under conditions of low absorbance. Strictly speaking, F is proportional to the number of absorbing molecules.

Curves such as Fig. 5.1 have been obtained experimentally. The range over which the emitted intensity is proportional to concentration has to be determined from a

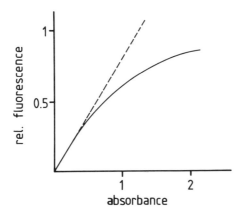

Fig. 5.1. Relation between absorbance and fluorescence, calculated for a homogeneously stained object.

calibration curve. One can assume that the concentration will be proportional to absorbance, because in fluorescence work usually only low concentrations are used. Two phenomena cause a reduced fluorescence at higher local absorbance values. The first is the *inner filter effect* or *excitation absorbance*, defined as the reduction of excitation intensity in the layers of a fluorescing object further from the light source, owing to absorption by the fluorophore. This is the result of high local absorbance. The fluorescing molecules are not all equally well situated to collect excitation light. The layer, nearest to the excitation light source receives more excitation light (I_0 is greater) than layers further from the light source. The second is *reabsorption*: emitted fluorescence light can be reabsorbed partially by surrounding fluorophores since for most fluorochromes absorption and emission spectra overlap to some extent. This can cause an additional reduction of fluorescence yield. To avoid the influence of this phenomenon, measurements should be performed at higher emission wavelengths (i.e. outside the overlap region of excitation and emission spectra).

To obtain, for example, the total DNA content in a cell nucleus stained with a DNA-specific fluorochrome, the total fluorescence intensity must be measured. This is equal to the sum of the local fluorescence intensities, provided that a linear relationship between the fluorescence intensity and the concentration exists. This has previously been seen to be true for low local absorbances and for measurements outside the overlap region of absorption and emission spectra. Contrary to absorption photometry, where scanning of the object is required to circumvent the 'distributional error', it is thus possible to measure the total fluorescence intensity and determine the fluorochrome concentration without measuring local values. This distinct difference between absorption and fluorescence photometry is illustrated in Fig. 5.2.

absorption   fluorescence

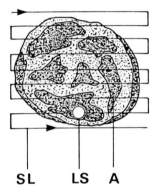 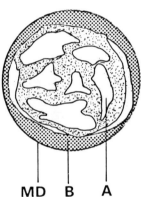

SL   LS   A   MD   B   A

Fig. 5.2. Comparison of fluorescence and absorbance photometry. (*Left*) the scanning method necessary for absorption photometry. This is a result of the logarithmic relation between light intensity and amount of substance. For fluorescence (*right*) total measurements are permitted for objects with low local absorbances. A = area; LS = light spot; SL = scan line; MD = measuring diaphragm; B = background.

5.2. Practical considerations for fluorescence measurements

A schematic diagram of the components of a microfluorometer is given in Fig. 5.3. Each component as well as the specimen will be discussed briefly in its relation to fluorescence measurement. This section finishes with measurement calibration.

5.2.1. Light source

The choice of light source is based on the excitation spectrum of the fluorochrome being measured and its quantum efficiency. Moreover, the light source must be

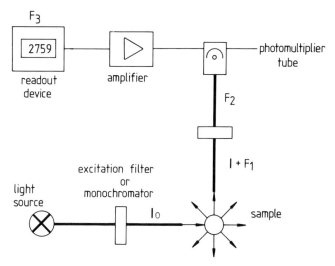

Fig. 5.3. Schematic diagram of the components of a microfluorometer. I_0 = exciting light intensity; I = unwanted exciting light; F_1 = emitted fluorescence; F_2 = output signal; F_3 = readout value.

stabilized to obtain constant exciting light. This is imperative since fluorescence intensity is proportional to exciting light intensity (see Section 5.1). Lamps with a direct-current stabilized-power supply offer a stabilized light source. For this reason the 100 W high-pressure mercury lamp (HBO 100) and the high-pressure xenon lamps (XBO) are suitable for microfluorometry.

5.2.2. Excitation filters

Light emitted by the light source passes through excitation filters which are chosen on the basis of the excitation spectrum of the fluorochrome being measured. In selecting these filters, one must realize that the spectrum of a fluorochrome can be influenced to a certain degree by conditions such as pH, ionic strength, and mounting medium of the preparation. This is one of the reaons for the necessity of standardized preparation procedures in quantitative FM. In general, narrow-band excitation filters are used in microfluorometry to avoid non-specific excitation of other molecules than the fluorophore to be measured. The exciting light intensity obtained is I_0 (Fig. 5.3).

5.2.3. Specimen

For *quantitative* FM, specimens are usually stained with fluorochromes for specific labelling of certain macromolecules. Standardized conditions for preparing specimens are needed for adequate microfluorometry. It is, for instance, known that the quantum efficiency is substantially influenced by the microenvironment of the fluorochrome. An example of this is *fluorescence quenching* by oxygen. Halogens can also cause quenching, owing to their influence on the electronic configuration of the fluorochrome. These effects are difficult to control. They form one reason for the need for internal standards as reference objects. Since the approximately linear relationship between fluorescence intensity and absorbance only exists at low local absorbance values, i.e. up to 0.2 (see Fig. 5.1), it is advisable to stain the specimens in such a way that the local absorbances are minimal.

Fading of the fluorescence may cause a serious problem in microfluorometry unless precautions are taken. Long exposure of the fluorophore prior to the measurement should be avoided. Objects to be measured may be selected by phase-contrast microscopy or, if necessary, using fluorescence excitation at very low light levels.

5.2.4. Chromatic beam splitter and emission (barrier) filters

Quantitative FM is predominantly performed using incident-light illumination for the following reasons:

1. It allows simple combination with other forms of transmitted-light microscopy (such as phase contrast), which can be used to select the objects (see above).
2. Easy maintenance of optimum alignment is possible, since the objective functions both as condenser and collecting lens.
3. Direction of emitted fluorescence of the surface of the specimen is towards the detection unit. In this set-up reabsorption is reduced and therefore a better linear relationship between measured fluorescence intensity and local dye concentration is provided.

In the epi-illumination set-up in quantitative FM, light collected at the emission side actually consists of unwanted excitation light plus emitted fluorescence $(I + F_1$; Fig. 5.3). To decrease the unwanted excitation light, a chromatic beam splitter in combination with a barrier filter is used, similar to routine FM. A second barrier filter of longer wavelength is often added to avoid the effect of the reabsorption of the part of the fluorescence light that overlaps with the absorption spectrum, on the measured intensity.

5.2.5. Detection unit

The emitted fluorescence F_1 becomes the output signal after passing barrier filters and a chromatic beam splitter. The output signal (F_2) can be measured by a light-sensing device, such as a photomultiplier (PM), which effectively measures the photons falling on the photon-sensitive part of the device. As shown in Fig. 5.3, the PM is equipped with amplifiers which can be used to amplify the output signal. The readout (F_3) value depends on the total photometric amplification; as a result, F_3 is sensitive to electronic fluctuations (for instance owing to temperature variation) of the detection unit. Moreover, the signal cannot be used in an absolute sense since the entire fluorescence microscope system and detection unit display a fluctuating noise element. This noise has a component inherent to the detection unit. The dark current of the PM is the signal measured when no light is offered. It must be calibrated to zero before measurement. Another noise component is the non-specific fluorescence, such as fluorescence from the slide and cover-slip, embedding medium, immersion oil, objective lenses, and autofluorescence. Stray light from optical components may cause non-specific signals to reach the detection unit. These noise components vary with the position of the preparation and in time. Measurements of fluorescence intensity are therefore always relative to a background level which must be determined simultaneously.

5.2.6. Measurement calibration

From Section 1 of this chapter it can be concluded that fluorescence intensity is a relative quantity, unlike absorbance, which is an absolutely defined quantity. This means that if fluorescence measurements taken at different days or obtained with different fluorometers, have to be compared, objects of constant or known fluorescence intensity should be used as standards. In principle, two types of standards can be distinguished, viz. *instrumentation standards* and *preparation standards*.

Instrumentation standards

These are permanent specimens which fluoresce reproducibly under a given set of physical conditions. If the optical system, filters, diaphragms etc., remain unchanged the only causes of change in fluorescence intensity would be a change in the brightness of the lamp, changes in sensitivity of the photodetector and changes in the electronic amplification system. These would all tend to result in a falling output signal. Moderate changes can usually be compensated by altering the setting of the amplifier to give a standard output reading. Rapid fluctuations, which are particularly common with mercury lamps, can be reduced by highly-stabilized power supplies and in some cases by reflecting a small fraction of the light from the lamp to a second photodetector which is used to regulate the power to the lamp, helping to keep its light output constant. A suitable standard is a slide made of uranyl glass which gives a strong yellow–green fluorescence. When the condenser or epi-objective is focused on the glass, the emission is almost independent of the level of focus or position on the slide, so long as the illuminated cone from the condenser or objective lies within the slide.

Another example of an instrumentation standard is a suspension of microdroplets of known volume and known fluorophore concentration in oil. The instrument can be calibrated as described above. An advantage of this system is that the actual measurement can be related to the absolute fluorophore concentration. Examples are the use of microdroplets of FITC for the calibration of immunofluorescence measurements.

Preparation standards

These are used to calibrate the fluorescent staining reaction. If a proper non-fading standard is available, instrumentation calibration is often no longer necessary. Preparation standards must contain a known and/or constant amount of macro-molecules that are fluorescently stained. Examples are the use of diploid cells as reference for DNA measurements. Most normal human cells are diploid and contain an amount of 2C DNA in their nucleus. These cells can thus be used as a reference to measure and calculate the DNA content of cells with an unknown amount of DNA, such as tumour cells. Also chicken nucleated red cells are used as reference cells for DNA measurements. Sepharose beads with a known amount of coupled antigen are suited as calibration objects for immunofluorescence studies.

5.3. Microscope fluorometry

In Fig. 5.4 a typical microfluorometer is shown schematically. It consists of a fluor-escence microscope with a number of adaptations which include the following.

1. Incident and transmitted illumination are provided by a high-pressure mercury lamp (HBO 100) and low-intensity tungsten halogen lamp (LL). Measurements can be performed with a stabilized light source, while objects can also be viewed by transmitted-light illumination. This permits the finding, centering and focusing of objects by means of the absorption image, before measure-ments are made on the fluorescence image. It minimizes the strong fading effects of high-intensity exciting light.
2. A substage bright field condenser is used for observing objects on the basis of absorption. For some purposes a dark-ground condenser can be used for pre-liminary observation with light that does not cause fading. The illumination can be changed at the last moment to high-intensity exciting light.
3. Illumination filters are chosen appropriate for the given fluorochrome(s). The transmitted-light illumination filters should permit viewing absorption images (no fading) or viewing fluorescing images at low-level excitation (minimal fading). Moreover, the contrast between fluorescing objects and background must be high for a good signal-to-noise ratio. This is achieved by a high-quality filter system which reduces unwanted light in the background. Specific, narrow excitation and emission filters and a chromatic beam splitter are required. A secondary selection filter (barrier filter) is positioned just before the photo-multiplier. Measurement is performed outside the overlap region of absorption and emission spectra (to reduce the influence of reabsorption). Bright images of the specimen can be visually controlled for estimating background light (unwanted excitation light or autofluorescence).
4. To measure fluorescence efficiently, moderate power objectives of high nu-merical aperture and low-power eyepieces are used for observation of the preparation. For weakly-fluorescing specimens especially, this is required for an adequate signal.

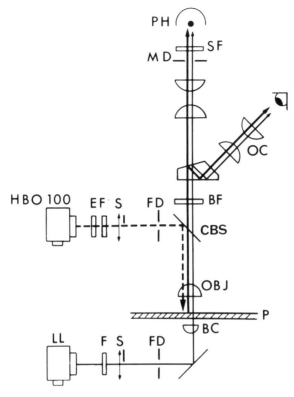

Fig. 5.4. Schematic diagram of a microfluorometer, showing combined transmitted- and incident-light illumination. HBO 100 = high-pressure mercury lamp; LL = low-intensity tungsten lamp; BC = bright field condenser; F = illumination filter; EF = narrow-excitation filter; BF = emission filter; SF = secondary selection (barrier) filter; OBJ = moderate power objective; OC = low-power eyepieces; P = preparation; FD = field diaphragms; MD = measuring diaphragm; S = shutters; PH = photodetector; CBS = chromatic beam splitter.

5. Effective collection of light and sensitive photodetectors are preferable to the use of very strong exciting light, which can cause rapid fading.
6. Field diaphragms have to be variable, so that searching can be performed with transmitted illumination, generally with the diaphragm open, while measurement is performed with the fluorescence excitation field diaphragm minimized. The variable measuring diaphragm can be fitted just around images of measured objects for minimum disturbance from background light.
7. Electronically-controlled, automatically-operated shutters prevent interference between the two illumination systems. Moreover, fluorescence measurements can be made with standard short exposure times (0.01–1 sec) by automatically opening and closing the shutters.
8. For accurate microfluorometry, three additional measurements are made. These are dark current of the photometer, background light outside the fluorescing object, and fluorescence of a standard fluorescing object for calibration.

5.4. Special microfluorometry instrumentation

In view of their widespread use, a number of special microfluorometers have been selected for description.

5.4.1. Scanning microscope fluorometers

Two types of available: *inverted microscope fluorometers* and *scanning microfluorometers*.

Inverted microscope fluorometers

Inverted microscopes have been manufactured with substage epi-illuminators. This permits fluorometry in various investigations requiring inverted microscopes, for example in studies dealing with cell cultures, fluids, or sediments. Immunological tests carried out in microtitre plates (96 wells), or in Terasaki-type trays (60 wells) are much-used examples of this type of investigation. Cells sediment to the flat bottom of the tray and can best be examined from below. The microfluorometer used is similar to conventional apparatus, except that the specimen is illuminated from below and the fluorescence is collected by a suitably-placed photodetector. Fig. 5.5 illustrates the light-beam path for an inverted microscope. The microscope can be equipped with computer-controlled stepping motors for moving the microscope stage to the measuring areas. This instrumentation is often used for the automatic readout of immunological cytotoxicity assays or enzyme-linked immunosorbent assay (ELISA) tests.

Scanning microfluorometers

For a number of applications, fluorescence measurements must be made in a localized manner, as opposed to total field measurements. Research involving not only the measurement of fluorescing objects but also acquisition of fluorescing images for pattern recognition, requires the use of scanning microfluorometers. The aim is to deduce size, shape, and intensity characteristics from local fluorescence intensity in the field illuminated with exciting light. One distinguishes *object scanners* and *image scanners*. In object scanners, either the specimen can be moved with reference to the light source (*stage scanners*) or the light is directed over the specimen (*flying spot scanners; mirror scanners*). Examples of image plane scanners are television systems or diode-array scanners.

The recent development of very rapid stages (for instance, a 10 000 Hz stage with 0.25 μm step-size) permits rapid scanning of fluorescing objects with minimum fading. A minicomputer or microprocessor can be used for automatic control of the microscope (stages; shutters) and for sorting measured values. Software programs can then be applied for analysis of the fluorescence intensity distribution.

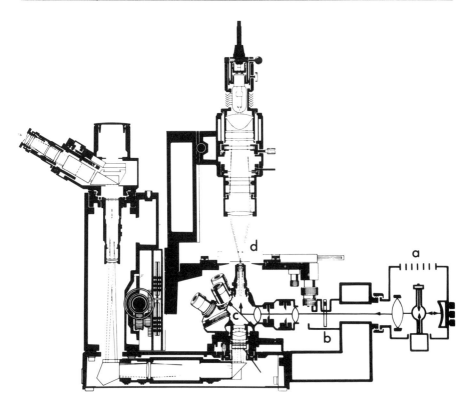

Fig. 5.5. Inverted fluorescence microscope. (a) = Light source; (b) = excitation filter; (c) = chromatic beam splitter; (d) = preparation.

An example of this is the labelling of neurotransmitters in tissue sections (either by immunological techniques or by the formaldehyde-induced fluorescence technique) with subsequent localization and quantification of the various neurotransmitters. With the advent of sensitive television cameras, the use of fluorescence scanning has increased. Sensitive camera tubes (silicon-intensified target camera tubes for instance) and image intensifiers permit scanning of even very weakly-fluorescing images. The high sensitivity can also be utilized for time-lapse studies of fluorescing images, since a very low excitation light level is adequate for visualization, thus resulting in minimum fading and long-time exposure potential.

5.4.2. Flow cytometry

The principle of flow cytometry is that cells in suspension are passed through a focused excitation beam of light, during which the generated light signals are measured by a detector.

In *epi-illumination systems*, cells are excited and measured at one side with one lens (Fig. 5.6). In *orthogonal systems*, excitation beam, flow stream, and measuring channel are oriented along three orthogonal axes (Fig. 5.7).

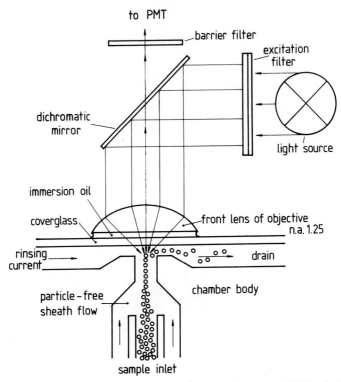

Fig. 5.6. Flow system with epi-illumination; n.a. = numerical aperture; PMT = photomultiplier tube.

Epi-illumination systems often use high numerical aperture lenses focused with oil immersion onto microcuvettes in which the cells flow through. Since high numerical aperture objectives are used, a large part of the emitted fluorescence light can be collected and measured. This permits the use of mercury arc lamps as an excitation light source.

In the orthogonal configuration, dry objectives are generally used, with long working distances and relatively high depths of field. A high-power laser-light source provides high-energy exciting light. The orthogonal configuration is highly effective if cells must be separated from the stream following measurement. The principle of individual particle sorting is accomplished by allowing the fluid stream to break off in microdroplets containing the particles. These droplets can be charged positively or negatively and then deflected in an electrostatic field. Sorting based on this principle is predominantly carried out with the orthogonal configuration.

The advantages of flow cytometry over other quantitative FM methods is the rapidity of measurements. Thousands of particles can easily be measured per second, offering a unique method for population studies. For such applications, stage microfluorometry is at present still too slow. Problems investigated by flow cytometry are, for example, in the area of proliferation kinetics of cells exposed to radiation, cytostatic drugs, etc. These studies are mostly based on DNA measurements. Data from flow cytometry are generally presented in the form of histograms (Fig. 5.8). By computer analysis of these histograms, information about the cell cycle (number of cells in G1, S, and G2 + M) can be obtained. Modern flow cytometers are computer-controlled and able to measure numerous parameters (six or more) simultaneously from one cell.

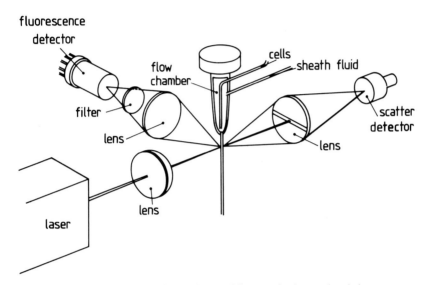

Fig. 5.7. Flow system with three orthogonal axes of flow, excitation, and emission.

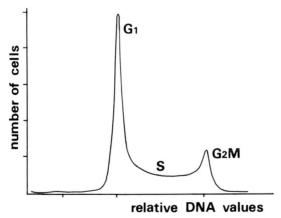

Fig. 5.8. DNA flow histogram of a cell population obtained by flow cytometry. The relationship between diploid cells (G1), cells in synthesis (S) and dividing cells (G2 + M) is shown. The X-axis shows the channel number (fluorescence intensity).

Bibliography

Piller, H. (1977). *Microscope photometry*. Springer-Verlag, Berlin, Heidelberg, New York.

Ploem, J. S. (1970). Standards for fluorescene microscopy. In *Standardization in immunofluorescence*, (ed. E.J. Holborrow), p. 137. Blackwell Scientific Publications, Oxford.

Ruch, F. (1970). Principles and some applications of cytofluorometry. In *Introduction to quantitative cytochemistry*, Vol. 2, (ed. G.L. Wied and G.F. Bahr), p. 431. Academic Press, New York.

Sernetz, M. and Thaer, A.A. (1973). Microcapillary fluorometry and standardization for microscope fluorometry. In *Fluorescence techniques in cell biology*, (ed. A.A. Thaer and M. Sernetz), p. 41. Springer-Verlag, New York.

Microspectrography

6.1. Instrumentation

Fluorescing dyes can show a different spectral behaviour in the unbound state (in solution in cuvettes) and bound state (to cellular components or natively-fluorescing cellular constituents). To determine the spectral characteristics of dyes bound to cell components or to identify autofluorescing cell components, a microscope is combined with a *spectrofluorometer*. This instrument is equipped with two mono-chromators, one for varying the excitation (absorption) wavelength and one for varying the emission wavelength. The emitted light is recorded with a photomulti-plier and observed on a graphic recorder oscilloscope or TV monitor. For con-venience, the monochromators are generally equipped with stepping motors working under computer control. The microscope has computer-controlled light shutters for the different light paths. For the registration of excitation and emission spectra, it is important that the fluorescence microscope has facilities for measuring very small areas of fluorescing objects (a few square micrometres, for example, in cells and tissues) in order to measure characteristics of just one particular fluoro-chrome in a specific area of the object. This is accomplished with optics that project the entrance slit of the monochromator in the microscopic image. The slit can be rotated and made longer, shorter, wider, or narrower for measuring emission and excitation spectra.

As *microspectrography* is a highly-specialized technique, the instrument as well as its use for measurement of spectra are only briefly described.

6.2. Measuring spectra

To measure excitation spectra, the fluorescence intensity is measured at a fixed wavelength. The monochromator is used to vary the excitation wavelength. The relative fluorescence intensity values can then be plotted as the excitation spec-trum. A number of errors must first be corrected for, however. The excitation light source has different light intensities at different wavelengths, and the optical system has different transmissions for each wavelength.

Emission spectra are recorded by exciting the specimen at a fixed wavelength and analysing the emission at various wavelengths using a monochromator and photomultiplier. The obtained spectra must be corrected for different sensitivity of the photomultiplier for different wavelengths and also for the varying transmission behaviour of the optics.

A microspectrograph is helpful in determining optimum filter combinations, especially in cases where two fluorochromes with overlapping colours must be measured separately. Besides this, spectral analysis can be performed for the identification of fluorescing components. Examples are certain neurotransmitter compounds which show minor differences in emission characteristics. These differences are generally too small for accurate visual identification, but can be identified by microspectrography.

Bibliography

Hirschberg, J.G., Wouters, A.W., Kohn, E., Kohen, C., Thorell, B., Eisenberg, B., Salmon, J.M. and Ploem, J.S. (1979). A high resolution grating microspectrofluorometer with topographic option for studies in living cells. In *Multichannel image detectors*, ACS Symposium Series, No. 102, (ed. Y. Talmi), p. 263. American Chemical Society.

Jotz, M.M., Gill, J.E. and Davis, D.T. (1976). A new optical multichannel microspectrofluorometer *Journal of Histochemistry and Cytochemistry,* 24, 91.

Ottenjann, K. (1981/1982). Verbesserungen bei der mikroskopphotometrischen Fluoreszenzmessungen an Kohlenmaceralen. *Zeiss Informationen (Oberkochen),* 26, 40.

Pearse, AGE. and Rost, F.W.D. (1968). A microspectrofluorometer with epi-illumination and photon counting; *Journal of Microscopy,* 89, 321.

Ploem, J.S., de Sterke, J.A., Bonnet, J. and Wasmund, H. (1974). A microspectrofluorometer with epi-illumination under computer control. *Journal of Histochemistry and Cytochemistry,* 22, 668.

Fluorescence photomicrography

7.1. Reciprocity failure

Fluorescence photomicrography (FP) can be performed with a system similar to that shown in Fig. 7.1. Besides the use of an automatic photomicrography microscope, simple non-automatic instruments can also be used provided that suitable light sources and filters are available.

One of the major problems involved in this type of photography is that most of the available films have been developed for work at relatively short exposure times (0.01–0.1 sec). For FP, exposure times of one or two magnitudes longer are necessary. Films have a reduced efficiency when exposed to low light levels for long exposure times. This means that a low light intensity (for example one arbitrary unit) during a long time (10 sec) will have less effect on the film than a high intensity

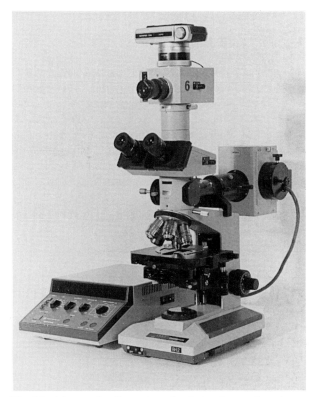

Fig. 7.1. An example of an automatic photomicrography microscope.

(for example 100 arbitrary units) for a short time (0.1 sec). This phenomenon is called the *reciprocity failure* (RF) of the film. The RF has two effects. First, the use of colour-reversal film at long exposures results in wrong colour reproduction of the photomicrograph, owing to the difference in the RF factor for the (usually three) different colour-sensitive layers of the film. The effect can be corrected by placing a *colour-compensating filter* in the light beam before exposure. Secondly, long exposure results in bleaching of the fluorochromes. This in turn necessitates longer exposure times, a vicious circle which is hard to avoid. Besides the use of extra sensitive films, everything possible should be done to obtain brightly-fluorescing microscopical images to reduce exposure times. This includes the following:

Use of lenses with moderate magnification and maximum numerical aperture.
Excitation with high-intensity light, at the absorption maximum of the fluorophore.
Use of a 0–100 per cent reflector (prism or mirror) which directs either all the light to the camera, or to the binocular eyepiece (for focusing).

7.2. Cameras and films

7.2.1. Fully-automatic cameras

These cameras are equipped with a built-in sensitive photomultiplier tube, through which exposure determination will take place during exposure. The camera therefore automatically compensates for fading of the specimen during exposure with exciting light. Exact exposure times can be determined for very small objects (down to a few per cent of the entire microscopic field). This is called *spot exposure* and facilitates photography of single objects in relatively large non-fluorescing surroundings. Simple camera systems are equipped with a less-sensitive photoresistor instead of a photomultiplier tube, and therefore will not give an exposure time reading for weak fluorescence. An accessory photometer can be used as an exposure meter for fluorescence.

Usually there is a knob to compensate for the reciprocity failure, which on the older German microscopes is indicated as the *Schwarzschild effekt*.

7.2.2. Manual cameras

These can also be used for FP, although exposure meters generally are not sensitive enough for correct readings. The use of these cameras thus has to be based on experience by trial and error.

7.2.3. Films

For selection of films, it must be realized that increased film sensitivity will lead to larger grains of silver in the negative, and in a loss of contrast and resolution. To increase a weak microscopic image contrast, a special high-contrast film can be used. Film processing also influences contrast, sensitivity, and resolution.

For colour FP, it is advisable to use reversal colour films. These yield direct positive colour transparencies after standardized reversal processing with resulting colours comparable to the original. From these transparencies colour prints can be made. The use of negative film is not recommended. These films are less sensitive and the preparation of prints from colour negatives is a rather subjective process. Since processing of films is commonly performed by commercial firms, this often leads to incorrect colour differentiation. If a colour negative is nevertheless required, it is helpful to provide the processing company with a colour print for comparison of colours. Suitable colour films for FP at long exposure times are the artificial (tungsten) light film types.

Bibliography

Eastman-Kodak (Rochester, New York) brochures on photomicrography include: *Photography through the microscope; Ultraviolet and fluorescence photography; Kodak black and white films for professional use; Kodak films for the amateur; Kodak colour films.*

Pearse, A.G.E. (1972). *Histochemistry: theoretical and applied*, Vol. 2, (3rd edn). Churchill-Livingstone, Edinburgh.

Schuit, H.R.E. (1970). Photomicrographic recording of immunofluorescence. In *Standardization in immunofluorescence*, (ed. E.J. Holborrow), p. 159. Blackwell, Oxford.

8

Trouble-shooting

8.1. General problems in fluorescence microscopy

1. High-pressure mercury or xenon arc lamp does not start.
(a) Check if the lamp-housing is still warm. If the lamp has been used shortly before, about 5 min will be needed before the lamp can be restarted.
(b) Are all leads properly secured? Open the lamp-housing and replace the bulb if necessary. *A xenon lamp is always under pressure and presents an explosion hazard*! Safety masks or safety glasses therefore are recommended; the same holds for a hot mercury lamp. Always allow lamps to cool down and *never* handle lamps with bare fingers.
(c) Check the fuses and the safety pin that protects from over-heating.

2. No exciting light observed passing through the objective.
(a) Is the shutter in the illumination pathway, or the illuminator, open?
(b) Is the illuminator in the right position so that light can pass excitation filter, chromatic beam splitter, and barrier filter?
(c) Is the field diaphragm open?
(d) Is the lamp properly aligned?

3. No emitted light is observed through the eyepieces.
(a) Is there an object in focus? If necessary, focus using transmitted light illumination.
(b) Are mirrors and filters in the right position?
(c) If a photocamera is connected to the microscope, is the prism set to direct light to the eyepieces or camera?
(d) If the fluorescence is very weak, darken the room and use low magnification high numerical aperture optics.
(e) Check the lamp for proper alignment.
(f) Check the hours of operation of the lamp. A mercury lamp may give very little light after its average lifetime.
(g) Has an extra (wrong) barrier filter been inserted?

4. A strong red background is observed.
(a) Check if the red absorbing BG 38 filter is present in the lamp-housing or in the fluorescence illuminator.
(b) Be sure that no unbound dye is present in the background.
(c) In the case of wet mounted preparations, check the mounting medium. If nail polish is used as a cement it should be a non-coloured type.

5. Unwanted excitation light.

(a) Use other excitation filter with better blocking characteristics for higher wavelengths, or use a combination of filters.

(b) Excite at lower wavelength than the optimum one, using the same barrier filter.

(c) Use a barrier filter effective at higher wavelengths. Sometimes a thicker filter is sufficient.

(d) Check autofluorescence of objective and immersion oil.

(e) Close the field diaphragm a little; note that the image contrast improves.

6. Poor image contrast.

(a) Use optics with minimum magnification and maximum numerical aperture.

(b) Close the field diaphragm a little to reduce stray light.

7. Observation of specimen is difficult owing to rapid fading.

(a) Darken the room and insert neutral-density filters in the lamp-housing to lower the effective excitation energy.

(b) Try higher wavelength or narrow-band exciting filter.

8.2. Difficulties in fluorescence photomicrography

1. Fluorescence is not bright enough for good quality photomicrography.

(a) Use low magnification and high numerical aperture optics.

(b) Use sensitive film (artificial light or tungsten-type colour films).

(c) Use a 100 per cent prism to direct all emission light to the camera. This reduces the effect of the reciprocity failure.

2. Wrong colour.

(a) Use appropriate colour-correction filters after attempting to improve the image intensity.

(b) Do not over-expose film.

(c) Ultraviolet or deep-violet unwanted exciting light is difficult to see, and may result in photographs with a blue colour contrast. Check if the correct barrier filter is present.

3. An overall reddish background on the film.

Use a SP 610 or SP 630 filter in front of the camera to block the far-red emission light which is normally not observed visually but registered by some films.

8.2. Difficulties in microfluorometry

1. Unexpected strong fluorescence intensity of the background is measured.

(a) Has the dark current been set to zero?

(b) Does the room light influence measured values?

(c) Do the filters leak unwanted excitation light?

(d) Has the field diaphragm been set to minimum size to reduce stray light?

(e) Check autofluorescence of immersion oil, filters, and objective.

2. *Unexpected strong variations in the measured values.*
(a) Are the objects susceptible to fading before measurements?
(b) Are both field and measuring diaphragm centered and set to minimum size?
(c) Is a stabilized light source used for excitation?
(d) Is there unbound dye present in the background? Be sure there is none.
(e) Has the lamp been set for Koehler illumination?
(f) Is the signal too strong for the detector? Place known neutral-density filters immediately in front of the detector. Check linearity of detector and amplifier.

Index